Book 4

Sure-fire Phonics

Ann Williams and Jim Rogerson

Illustrated by Oxford Illustrators Limited

Wheaton

A Division of Pergamon Press

A. Wheaton & Company Limited
A Division of Pergamon Press
Hennock Road, Exeter EX2 8RP

Pergamon Press Ltd
Headington Hill Hall, Oxford OX3 0BW

Pergamon Press Inc.
Maxwell House, Fairview Park, Elmsford, New York 10523

Pergamon Press Canada Ltd.
Suite 104, 150 Consumers Road, Willowdale, Ontario M2J 1P9

Pergamon Press (Australia) Pty Ltd.
P.O. Box 544, Potts Point, N.S.W. 2011

Pergamon Press GmbH
Hammerweg 6, D–6242 Kronberg
Federal Republic of Germany

First published 1980

Reprinted 1982

Printed in Great Britain by A. Wheaton & Co. Ltd, Exeter (TS)
ISBN 0 08 024347 9

Contents

sh as in **sh**ip

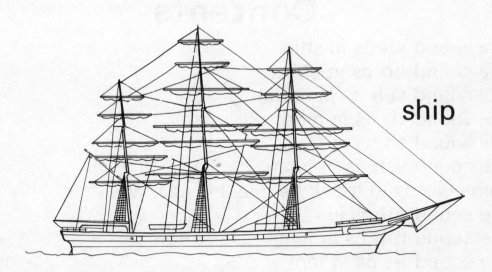

ship

Read these words. Write them in your exercise book.

1. **ship**	2. shin	3. shock	4. shop
5. shot	6. shall	7. shell	8. shut
9. dish	10. fish	11. wish	12. cash
13. mash	14. mesh	15. hush	16. rush

Choose the right word to complete the sentence.
Write the sentence in your exercise book.

1. Jack hit Tom on the _____.   (shot, shin)

2. Sam had a big _____.   (shell, shall)

3. The shop is _____.   (ship, shut)

4. Dad has a _____ in his net.   (fish, dish)

5. Ron has a _____ on his leg.   (rush, rash)

6. I _____ I had a lot of cash.   (dash, wish)

ch as in **ch**ick

chick

Read these words. Write them in your exercise book.

1. **chick**	2. chin	3. chip	4. chill
5. chilly	6. chap	7. chat	8. check
9. chess	10. chug	11. chum	12. chop
13. rich	14. much	15. such	

Choose the right word to complete the sentence.
Write the sentence in your exercise book.

1. Ben is Dick's _____.   (chat, chum)

2. Put the _____ in the pan, Tom.   (chips, chins)

3. Jack is not a _____ man.   (much, rich)

4. Pam will _____ the logs.   (chess, chop)

5. Dad is _____ a big man.   (such, much)

6. Ann's hen has a _____.   (check, chick)

tch as in ma**tch**

match

Read these words. Write them in your exercise book.

1. **match**   2. batch   3. catch   4. hatch

5. latch   6. patch   7. fetch   8. ditch

9. hitch   10. pitch   11. witch   12. Dutch

13. hutch

Choose the right word to complete the sentence.
Write the sentence in your exercise book.

1. The _____ had a pet cat.   (witch, pitch)

2. Mum had a _____ of buns.   (batch, latch)

3. The hen will _____ the eggs.   (patch, hatch)

4. Can Pam _____ the dog?   (catch, hatch)

5. Dan had a _____ box.   (fetch, match)

6. The _____ is full of mud.   (hitch, ditch)

th as in moth

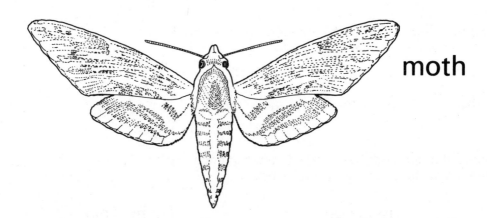

moth

Read these words. Write them in your exercise book.

1. **moth**   2. thick   3. thin   4. thud

5. thug   6. Beth

Choose the right word to complete the sentence.
Write the sentence in your exercise book.

1. Jack is a _____ lad.   (thug, thin)

2. It is a _____ rug.   (thick, thud)

3. A _____ is on the mat.   (thin, moth)

4. The _____ robs Pam.   (thud, thug)

5. _____ has a doll.   (Beth, Moth)

6. Tom fell in the _____ mud.   (thud, thick)

th as in that

Read these words. Write them in your exercise book.

1. than   2. that   3. them   4. then

5. this   6. with

Choose the right word to complete the sentence.
Write the sentence in your exercise book.

1. _____ cap is wet.   (Them, This)

2. I hit _____ bell.   (than, that)

3. Jack ran, _____ I ran.   (them, then)

4. Put the box _____ the sack.   (with, that)

5. _____ pan is hot.   (This, With)

6. Put _____ back.   (with, them)

wh as in **wh**ip

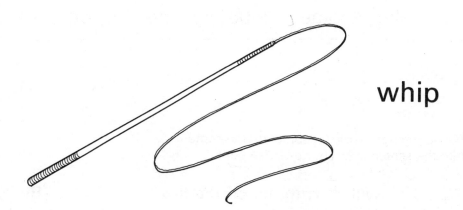

whip

Read these words. Write them in your exercise book.

1. **whip**   2. whiff   3. whizz   4. which

5. whack   6. when

Choose the right word to complete the sentence.
Write the sentence in your exercise book.

1. _____ I am ill, I am sad.   (When, Which)

2. Pat has a _____ and top.   (whiff, whip)

3. Pam will get off the ship _____ it docks.   (when, whiff)

4. Beth will _____ the eggs in the dish.   (whip, whack)

5. _____ is the bad lad?   (Whizz, Which)

Some words to learn:

he	me	be	she	we

Choose the right word to complete the sentence.
Write the sentence in your exercise book.

1. _____ will sit with me on the box.   (Be, She)

2. _____ dug a ditch.   (We, Me)

3. _____ shot a shell at the ship.   (Be, He)

4. If Tom hits _____ I will yell.   (we, me)

5. _____ will lock the box.   (Be, We)

6. _____ ran up the hill.   (He, Me)

7. She will _____ on the red bus.   (be, he)

8. _____ hit me with a rod.   (We, He)

qu as in quill

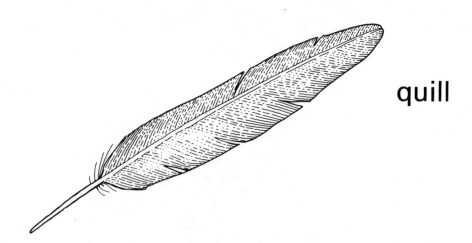

quill

Read these words. Write them in your exercise book.

1. **quill**   2. quick   3. quin   4. quit

5. quiz   6. quack   7. quell

Choose the right word to complete the sentence.
Write the sentence in your exercise book.

1. Be _____, Beth.   (quiz, quick)

2. Pass the _____ pen, Jim.   (quill, quin)

3. A dog can not _____.   (quell, quack)

4. Tom _____ his job at the mill.   (quit, quell)

5. Jill is not as _____ as Beth.   (quick, quiz)

6. Dad will not _____ his job.   (quin, quit)

mp as in lamp

lamp

Read these words. Write them in your exercise book.

1. **lamp**	2. camp	3. damp	4. ramp
5. bump	6. dump	7. hump	8. jump
9. lump	10. pump	11. thump	12. mumps
13. imp	14. chimp	15. hemp	16. romp

Choose the right word to complete the sentence.
Write the sentence in your exercise book.

1. It is _____ in the shed.   (damp, camp)

2. Nick had a _____ on his leg.   (hump, lump)

3. Pam has _____.   (mumps, ramps)

4. The pup can _____ on the rock.   (jump, dump)

5. Ron has a _____.   (limp, imp)

6. Ann lit the wick in the _____.   (damp, lamp)

nt as in tent

tent

Read these words. Write them in your exercise book.

1. **tent**	2. bent	3. dent	4. lent
5. rent	6. sent	7. went	8. hint
9. lint	10. mint	11. tint	12. ant
13. pant	14. hunt	15. punt	16. font

Choose the right word to complete the sentence.
Write the sentence in your exercise book.

1. The latch is _____.   (bent, rent)

2. The men will _____ the fox.   (font, hunt)

3. I _____ on the bus with Mum.   (went, sent)

4. The dog _____ when it runs.   (pants, rants)

5. The lads put up a big _____.   (tint, tent)

6. Sally will pick the _____.   (mint, hint)

nk as in tank

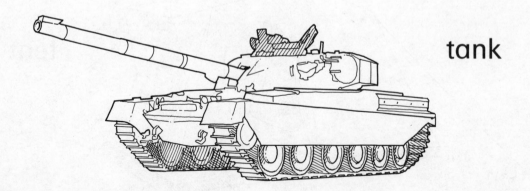

tank

Read these words. Write them in your exercise book.

1. **tank**	2. bank	3. hank	4. rank
5. sank	6. thank	7. link	8. mink
9. pink	10. rink	11. sink	12. think
13. wink	14. bunk	15. junk	16. sunk

Choose the right word to complete the sentence.
Write the sentence in your exercise book.

1. The _____ is shut.   (sank, bank)

2. I _____ I can cut that log.   (think, thank)

3. Put the pot in the _____, Ben.   (sink, sunk)

4. Tom has a _____-bed.   (bunk, wink)

5. The man will fill the _____.   (tank, hank)

6. Pat will sit on the mossy _____.   (rank, bank)

nd as in hand

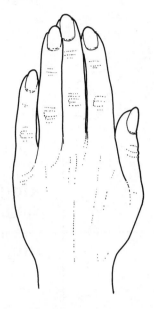

hand

Read these words. Write them in your exercise book.

1. **hand**   2. and   3. band   4. land

5. sand   6. end   7. bend   8. lend

9. mend   10. send   11. bond   12. fond

13. pond   14. fund

Choose the right word to complete the sentence.
Write the sentence in your exercise book.

1. Dad cut his _____ on the latch.   (hand, and)

2. Jack is in a jazz _____.   (land, band)

3. Dad can _____ Dick a rucksack.   (bend, lend)

4. Mick will _____ the pig pen.   (mend, end)

5. Fill the sack with _____.   (land, sand)

6. Dick fell in the _____.   (bond, pond)

13

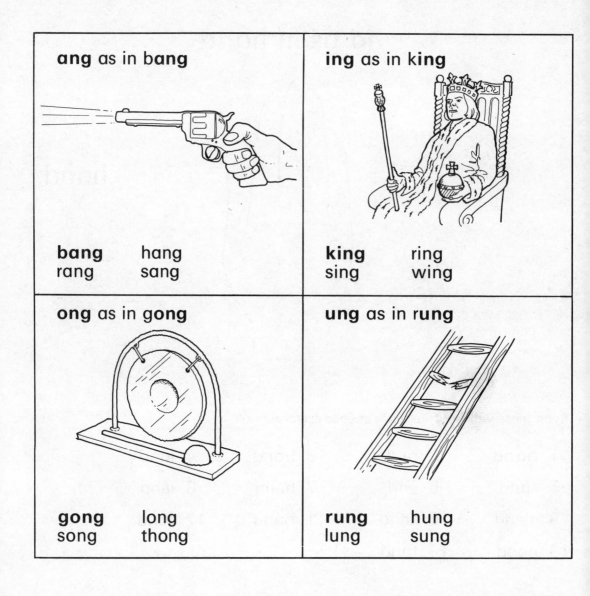

ang as in b**ang**	**ing** as in k**ing**
bang hang rang sang	**king** ring sing wing
ong as in g**ong**	**ung** as in r**ung**
gong long song thong	**rung** hung lung sung

Choose the right word to complete the sentence.
Write the sentence in your exercise book.

1. The duck's _____ is cut.   (wing, sing)

2. This is Ann's _____.   (king, ring)

3. Tom _____ his hat on the peg.   (lung, hung)

4. Ron's _____ ran up the hill.   (gang, hang)

5. The shell went _____.   (rang, bang)

6. Pam _____ the song well.   (gang, sang)

Read these **ing** words. Write them in your exercise book.

1. banging
2. catching
3. thanking
4. kicking
5. ringing
6. singing
7. thinking
8. locking
9. passing
10. begging
11. felling
12. getting
13. digging
14. filling
15. fitting
16. hitting
17. hopping
18. jogging
19. shopping
20. humming

Choose the right word to complete the sentence.
Write the sentence in your exercise book.

1. Jim is _____ logs.   (chopping, hopping)

2. Ann is _____ with Mum.   (ringing, shopping)

3. Tim is _____ in the dock.   (fishing, batting)

4. The dog is _____.   (begging, filling)

5. Dad is _____.   (getting, digging)

6. The hen is _____ the eggs.   (sinking, jogging, hatching)

7. Pam is _____ a song.   (singing, bobbing, biffing)

8. Pat is _____ on the mat.   (hitting, fitting, sitting)

Some words to learn:

they	said	are

Choose the right word to complete the sentence.
Write the sentence in your exercise book.

1. "The men are pushing the van," _____ Ted.   (sid, said)

2. They _____ putting up the tent.   (are, am)

3. Are _____ catching fish?   (them, they)

4. "I am going with Tom," _____ Jack.   (said, sad)

5. _____ the ducks on the pond?   (Is, Are)

6. Ron _____, "The sacks are wet."   (sad, said)

7. The dogs _____ licking the dish.   (am, are)

8. _____ are sending Jill a box.   (Them, They)

It as in belt

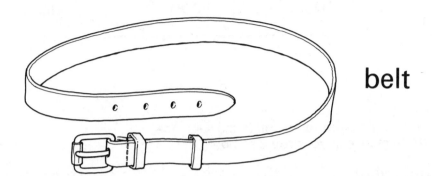

belt

Read these words. Write them in your exercise book.

1. **belt**   2. Celt   3. felt   4. melt

5. pelt   6. hilt   7. kilt   8. quilt

9. silt   10. tilt   11. wilt

Choose the right word to complete the sentence.
Write the sentence in your exercise book.

1. The _____ fell off the bed.   (quilt, wilt)

2. Mum has a long _____.   (kilt, silt)

3. Ben _____ sad when his dog ran off. (pelt, felt)

4. Will the sun _____ the jelly?   (melt, belt)

5. Polly has a red _____.   (hilt, belt)

6. The pup can _____ the dish.   (tilt, gilt)

Some words to learn:

to	who	do

Choose the right word to complete the sentence.
Write the sentence in your exercise book.

1. Jack went _____ the hut.   (who, to)

2. _____ will ring the bells?   (Who, Do)

3. I _____ not wish to camp in this tent.   (do, to)

4. _____ is hitting my cat?   (Do, Who)

5. I _____ not think Jock has a kilt.   (to, do)

6. Ron is running _____ catch the bus.   (do, to)

7. _____ is sitting in the bus with Mum?   (Who, Do)

8. Tom went _____ bed.   (who, to)

a as in cake

cake

Read these words. Write them in your exercise book.

1. **cake**	2. bake	3. lake	4. make
5. shake	6. sale	7. tale	8. date
9. mate	10. save	11. wave	12. game
13. name	14. case	15. chase	16. shade

Choose the right word to complete the sentence.
Write the sentence in your exercise book.

1. The box is _____ with me. (safe, sale)

2. Do not let the dog _____ the hens. (chase, chafe)

3. Mum puts Dad's hat in the _____. (cape, case)

4. "I am _____," said Bill. (late, lake)

5. "I _____ dogs," said the man. (hake, hate)

6. "Shut the _____," said Dad. (gate, gale)

i as in kite

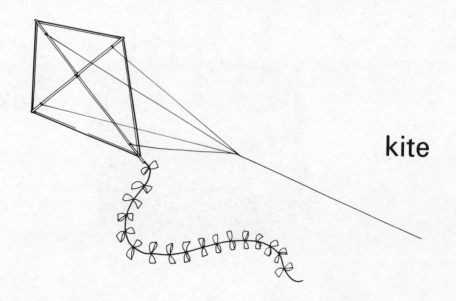

kite

Read these words. Write them in your exercise book.

1. **kite**   2. hide   3. ride   4. side

5. tide   6. wide   7. hike   8. like

9. pike   10. fine   11. mine   12. vine

13. wine   14. dive   15. five   16. time

Choose the right word to complete the sentence.
Write the sentence in your exercise book.

1. I am five, but Ben is _____.   (nine, mine)

2. "This is Tom's _____," said Jack.   (whine, wife)

3. A _____ is a fish.   (pike, pile)

4. Pip can _____ into the lake.   (dine, dive)

5. "I like the _____," said Polly.   (bike, bite)

6. Sally will _____ the cups.   (wipe, while)

o as in rose

rose

Read these words. Write them in your exercise book.

1. **rose**	2. hose	3. nose	4. dole
5. hole	6. mole	7. pole	8. coke
9. poke	10. woke	11. hope	12. Pope
13. rope	14. note	15. vote	16. home

Choose the right word to complete the sentence.
Write the sentence in your exercise book.

1. Dad went _____ with Mum. (hope, home)

2. A _____ is a fish. (rope, sole)

3. Ted _____ up at six. (woke, vote)

4. Jill put the _____ in Jenny's bag. (nose, note)

5. Jack has a cut on his _____. (nose, hose)

6. Molly _____ on Ben's bike. (robe, rode)

u as in **cube**

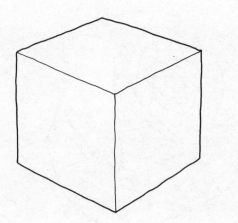

cube

Read these words. Write them in your exercise book.

1. **cube**   2. tube   3. cute   4. jute

5. mute   6. use   7. fuse   8. dune

9. tune   10. duke   11. mule   12. nude

Choose the right word to complete the sentence.
Write the sentence in your exercise book.

1. The _____ gave a ring to the king.   (duke, cube)

2. I can sing this _____ .   (tube, tune)

3. The _____ had a pack on its back.   (mule, mute)

4. The _____-box is in the pub.   (juke, jute)

5. Pam and Pat dug in the sand _____ .   (dunes, dukes)

6. A _____ is like a pipe.   (tune, tube)

Some words to learn:

was	were	have

Choose one of these words to complete each sentence.
Write the sentence in your exercise book.

was   were   have

1. He _____ sad.

2. They _____ happy.

3. _____ they made the chips?

4. She _____ thin.

5. _____ they got a big tent?

6. They _____ ringing the bells.

7. Jack _____ singing with Jim.

8. The hens _____ sitting on the eggs.

9. I _____ got mumps.

Find a rhyming word. Write it in your exercise book. The picture will help you.

1. fish, wish   _____

2. pitch, hitch, ditch   _____

3. ill, bill, fill   _____

4. tan, than, ban   _____

5. nip, lip, pip   _____

6. ramp, camp, damp   _____

7. bent, lent, dent   _____

8. mink, pink, rink   _____

9. hilt, wilt, tilt   _____

10. lake, bake, make   _____

11. hike, like, Mike   _____

12. pole, hole, dole   _____

Some words to learn:

you   your

Choose one of these words to complete each sentence.
Write the sentence in your exercise book.

you   your

1. Have _____ cut your leg?

2. "_____ dog is sick," said the vet.

3. Shall I mend _____ bike?

4. Are _____ hot?

5. Have _____ got a match?

6. Is Tom _____ chum?

7. Is this _____ hat?

8. Can _____ catch the dog?

9. Put _____ hat on the peg.

Rearrange these jumbled letters into words that match the pictures.
Write the words in your exercise book.

chwit   1. _____

othm   2. _____

desh   3. _____

tike   4. _____

ores   5. _____

clok   6. _____

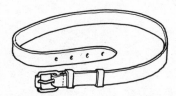

lteb   7. _____

gnri   8. _____

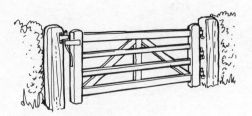

teag   9. _____

ecka   10. _____

Find the sentence that matches each picture.
Write the sentence in your exercise book.

Sally has a doll.

Jack lit a lamp.

This is a big tank.

A thin man sat on a tub.

A fox ran to the shed.

Ted hangs up his cap.

Bill and Ben camp in the tent.

Ken pulls the bell rope.

1.

2.

3.

4.

5.

6.

7.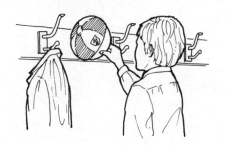

8.

"Get off that bike," said Sid. "It's mine."

"No, it's not," said Pam. "It's Ken's bike."

"It's not mine," said Ken. "I think it's Ben's."

"Ben has not got a bike like that," said Sid.

"His bike is red and white. This bike is pink
and white. It's mine."

Pam got off the bike. "Take your bike, then,"
she said. "I'm going home."

Answer these questions in your exercise book. Write full sentences.

1. Was Ben riding the bike?

2. Did Pam think it was Ken's bike?

3. Did Sid go home?

4. Was Pam riding Sid's bike?

5. Did Pam go home?

6. Was the bike red and white?

Jack's Code

a	c	d	e	i	k	l	m
□	○	△	~	▭			◇	◠

n	o	p	r	s	t	u	w
◺	◿	◡	ʕ	◹	◖	×	+

Can you read these words?
Write the answers in your exercise book.

1. Ben did not have his ◠□◡ .

2. Pam ◹□▭△ that Bill had ◖□|~◺ it.

3. Bill said it +□◹ in the ◖~◺◹ but

   it was ◺◹◖ .

4. "It is in your ʕ×○|◹□○|," said △□△ .

5. +□◹ ▭◖ ?

29

Draw these crosswords in your exercise book.

Across

3.

4.

6.

Down

1.

2.

3.

5.

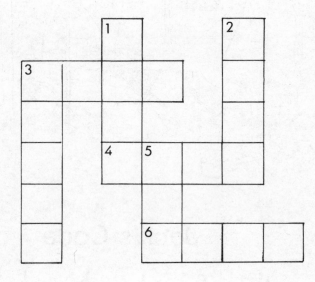

Across

1.

4.

5.

7.

Down

1.

2.

3.

6.